C000084604

Supporting
Writing
Skills

FOR AGES 8–9

Introduction

Supporting Writing Skills is aimed at all those who work with children who have been identified as needing 'additional' or 'different' literacy support. It can be used by anyone working with children who fall into this category, whether you are a teacher, classroom assistant or parent.

Typically the eight to nine year-old children for whom the book is intended will be working at the levels expected of Year 3 children or may simply need extra help in tackling the level of work appropriate for Year 4. Their difficulties may be short term, and can be overcome with extra practice and support on a one-to-one or small group basis, or they may be long term, where such support enables them to make progress but at a level behind their peer group.

The activities in this book provide exactly what these children need – plenty of writing activities linked to their work in other aspects of literacy. All the activities provide great opportunities for speaking and listening and these sometimes include simple drama activities based on role-play. Most pages include reading practice in addition to the main writing task. Each activity page includes brief Notes for teachers so that the pages can be picked up and used quickly and effectively.

The 2006 Framework for teaching Literacy lists twelve strands for literacy development. Strands 1 to 4 concern Speaking and Listening; Strands 5 to 12 concern Reading and Writing. The writing activities in this book have been created to match many of the key elements of the Framework's reading and writing strands for Year 3 and Year 4:

5. Special note: our activities reflect the move from word recognition to language comprehension but we recognise that some lower ability pupils will still need some support with decoding and encoding

6. Spell high frequency and medium frequency words; spell unfamiliar words using known conventions including grapheme-phoneme correspondences and morphological rules; develop a range of personal strategies for learning new and irregular words

7. Infer consequences in logical explanations; using syntax, context and word structure to build their store of vocabulary as they read for meaning

8. Empathise with characters

9. Make decisions about form and purpose; use beginning, middle and end to write narratives in which events are sequenced logically and conflicts resolved; write non-narrative texts using structures of different text types; select and use a range of technical and descriptive vocabulary; use settings and characterisation to engage readers' interests

10. Signal sequence, place and time to give coherence; group related material into paragraphs

11. Compose sentences using adjectives, verbs and nouns for precision, clarity and impact; clarify meaning through the use of exclamation marks and speech marks; use commas to mark clauses, and use the apostrophe for possession

12. Write with consistency in the size and proportion of letters and spacing within and between words, using the correct formation of handwriting joins.

Children generally achieve the greatest success in an atmosphere of support and encouragement. Praise from a caring adult can be the best reward for the children's efforts. The worksheets and activities in this book will provide many opportunities for children to enjoy these successes. The development of a positive attitude and the resulting increase in self-esteem will help them with all of their schoolwork.

Andrew Brodie: Supporting Writing Skills © A & C Black Publishers Ltd. 2007

This book consists of three main sections:

Section 1 (pages 6–28)

Worksheets 1 to 23 provide many opportunities for creating simple sentences then more complex sentences. Sentences with clear punctuation are modelled for the pupils and the accompanying activities promote the construction of accurate sentences that start with capital letters and end with full stops. Many activities include the use of more advanced punctuation: speech marks, question marks and exclamation marks.

Several pages include dictation exercises. These help children both to identify the sounds in particular words to assist with their spelling and to 'hear' the punctuation. By listening carefully to the sentences dictated by the teacher the children can spot where to use full stops, commas, exclamation marks and question marks.

Section 2 (pages 29–48)

This section consists of two longer writing exercises. The child is asked to complete short paragraphs that are provided in draft form with some words missing – these words can be selected from a range of words provided by rolling a dice. From this speaking, listening and reading activity the children move on to rewriting the text within a simple 'book' presentation. Further templates are provided to enable the children to create independent texts.

Section 3 (pages 49–64)

An important resource contained within this book is the dictionary that can be created from the final fourteen sheets. This contains all the high frequency words recommended for Key Stage 1 and the medium frequency words for Key Stage 2, together with all the additional words used in this book. The dictionary can be used by the child when working on the worksheets.

Each page of the dictionary has spaces for the child to write her/his own spellings – this is an excellent way of encouraging the child to use her/his phonic knowledge to spell new words. When a child needs a word, help her/him to find the correct page of the dictionary then ask her/him to attempt the word by segmenting it into its phonemes. Give the child lots of praise where s/he is successful even in part of a word then write the word correctly on the line next to her/his attempt, stressing the phonemes and pointing out the graphemes that represent these.

Strands of objectives for Literacy in the Primary Framework

On the Contents page we have listed which strand each worksheet addresses.

1. Speaking

2. Listening and responding

3. Group discussion and interaction

4. Drama

5. Word recognition: decoding (reading) and encoding (spelling)
   (Note: this strand ceases to be used after year2/year3)

6. Word structure and spelling

7. Understanding and interpreting texts

8. Engaging with and responding to texts

9. Creating and shaping texts

10. Text structure and organisation

11. Sentence structure and punctuation

12. Presentation

Contents

Andrew Brodie: Supporting Writing Skills © A & C Black Publishers Ltd. 2007

Record and Review

Name: _____   Date of birth: _____

Teacher: _____   Class: _____

Support assistant: _____

Code of Practice stage: _____   Date targets set: _____

Target

1 _____

2 _____

3 _____

4 _____

Review

Target

1 _____

_____

_____   Target achieved? ☐ Date: _____

2 _____

_____

_____   Target achieved? ☐ Date: _____

3 _____

_____

_____   Target achieved? ☐ Date: _____

4 _____

_____

_____   Target achieved? ☐ Date: _____

Name: _____   **Date:** _____

What is your full name?

_____

When is your birthday? _____

In what year were you born? _____

What is your address?

_____

_____

_____

_____

What is the name of your school?

_____

Who is your class teacher?

_____

Who else teaches you?

_____

Can you describe your family?

_____

_____

_____

_____

Notes for teachers

This worksheet provides lots of opportunities for getting to know a new pupil. Discuss each question before helping her/him to write the answers. Encourage her/him to spot the question mark at the end of each sentence but also to notice how each question starts and how each question 'sounds'. The child may not know her/his own address or date of birth. It would be a good idea to have these details to hand so that you can provide the information. Some of the spellings the child will need can be found in the dictionary created from the Resource sheets on pages 51–64. Any new words can be entered in the dictionary with your help. Some children will find the task of describing their family extremely difficult and will need prompts regarding parents, sisters, brothers, grandparents, etc. When s/he is ready to start help her/him to compose complete sentences and then to write them down, remembering capital letters and full stops as appropriate.

Andrew Brodie: Supporting Writing Skills © A & C Black Publishers Ltd. 2007

What do you like doing at school?

_____

_____

What do you not like doing at school?

_____

_____

_____

What do you like doing at home?

_____

_____

_____

What do you not like doing at home?

_____

_____

_____

Can you describe your home?

_____

_____

_____

_____

Notes for teachers

This worksheet provides more practice in recognising and answering questions. If possible, find a microphone and conduct a mock television interview asking the child the questions on the worksheet before showing them to her/him. Help the child to read the question sentences. Point out that each sentence starts with a capital letter because all sentences do and that all the question sentences end with question marks. Encourage the child to write full sentences, ensuring that each starts with a capital letter and ends with a full stop. Some of the spellings the child will need can be found in the dictionary created from the Resource sheets on pages 51–64. Any new words can be entered in the dictionary with your help. Some children will find the task of writing the sentences extremely difficult simply because they cannot think of ideas – help her/him with these. For the first sentence you could give some prompts, such as asking whether s/he likes sport, art, working on the computer, etc. For the question regarding what s/he likes doing at home you could provide suggestions such as watching television, playing in the garden, playing on the computer, etc. For the description of home you could ask whether s/he lives in a house, bungalow or flat; whether s/he has her/his own room; whether s/he has a garden, etc.

Name: _____   Date: _____

Read the sentences below. They are the replies to some questions. Try to work out what the questions were.

Q _____

_____

A Oh, yes thank you. I had a lovely weekend.

Q _____

_____

A In the morning I went shopping and in the afternoon I went to watch the match.

Q _____

_____

A Yes, two nil.

Q _____

_____

A After tea we went to the cinema to see the new Harry Potter film. I was very tired when we got in so I went straight to bed.

Notes for teachers

Read through the sentences with the child, pointing out that they all start with capital letters and end with full stops. Explain that **Q** and **A** are short forms of *question* and *answer*. Help the child to work out what each question might have been. The child may think of better ones but here are some possibilities: Did you have a nice weekend? What did you do on Saturday? Did your team win? What did you do in the evening? Make sure that the child starts each question with a capital letter and ends it with a question mark. Having worked out what the questions were, look again at the answers e.g. *In the morning I went shopping and in the afternoon I went to watch the match.* This could have been written as two separate sentences: *In the morning I went shopping. In the afternoon I went to watch the match.*
However, the word 'and' was used to make one sentence. Look at the final answer, which consists of two complex sentences. Can the child work out how each of these sentences could have been written as two sentences? Can s/he identify how each of the sentences has been written to include two pieces of information? As an extension activity, the child could continue the conversation.

Name: **Date:**

Read the questions below. Think about some answers
to the questions.
When you are ready, write
the answers down.

Q Did you have a good weekend?

A _____

_____

Q What did you do in the daytime on Saturday?

A _____

_____

Q What did you do on Saturday evening?

A _____

_____

Q What did you do on Sunday?

A _____

_____

Notes for teachers
Before asking the child to answer the questions read them through with her/him pointing out that they all start with capital
letters and end with question marks. Remind her/him that **Q** and **A** are short forms of *question* and *answer*. Help the child to
compose some answers to the questions, encouraging her/him to use complex sentences. Look again at Worksheet 3, pointing
out the complex sentences that were used in reply to some of the questions. Some children will find the task of writing the
sentences extremely difficult simply because they cannot think of ideas. Help her/him with these, perhaps by saying what you
did at the weekend. Alternatively, you could encourage the child to think of imaginative answers, building up a 'story' about
an imaginary weekend. As an extension activity, the child could continue the conversation.

Name: _____ **Date:** _____

Read the conversation that Jim and Tom are having on the telephone.

"Hello Tom," said Jim.
"Hello Jim," said Tom.
"What are you doing this afternoon?" asked Jim.
"I am going to play football," replied Tom.
"Can I come?" asked Jim.
"Yes. I will see you later," said Tom.

Look carefully at each line of the conversation as you are going to write it out on Worksheet 6.

Notes for teachers
This is an introductory worksheet to be used before dictating the conversation to the child to write on Worksheet 6. You may like to role play this conversation with the child. To do this successfully it is a good idea to highlight each boy's speech in a different colour, colouring only the words that are spoken i.e. the words contained within the speech marks. Now look at the sentences carefully with the child. Encourage her/him to notice that:
• the words spoken are contained between the speech marks
• every sentence starts with a capital letter
• the sentences do not end at the end of the spoken section
• the closing speech marks are never alone – they always have a comma or a question mark before them
• different words are used before the speaker's name e.g. 'said', 'asked', 'replied'
• a new line is started where a different person speaks
When you think the child is ready give her/him a copy of Worksheet 6.

Andrew Brodie: Supporting Writing Skills © A & C Black Publishers Ltd. 2007

Name: _____   **Date:** _____

worksheet
6

Listen to your teacher.
Write the conversation that Jim and Tom
are having on the telephone.
The conversation has been started for you.

"Hello Tom," said Jim.
"Hello Jim," said Tom.

_____

_____

_____

_____

_____

_____

_____

_____

_____

_____

Notes for teachers
This worksheet should be used after Worksheet 5. You may decide to show the child Worksheet 5 again during the course
of the dictation. Use Worksheet 5 for the dictation text and the rules that should be applied when the child writes. Before
dictating the conversation to the child, remind her/him of the 'rules' for writing down conversation:
• the words spoken are contained between speech marks
• every sentence starts with a capital letter
• the sentences do not end at the end of the spoken section
• the closing speech marks are never alone – they always have a comma or a question mark before them
• different words are used before the speaker's name e.g. 'said', 'asked', 'replied'
• a new line is started where a different person speaks
You may need to dictate the conversation several times. Encourage the child to write using the school's handwriting style.
As an extension activity, the child could continue the conversation further.

Name: _____   **Date:** _____

Read the conversation that Daisy and Maisy are having on the telephone.

"Hello, is that Daisy?" said Maisy.

"Yes, who's that?" asked Daisy.

"It's Maisy," said Maisy.

"Oh, hello Maisy. What are you doing this evening?"

"I'm not doing anything," replied Maisy.

"You are lazy Maisy!" laughed Daisy.

"Don't be crazy Daisy!" cried Maisy.

Both girls giggled.

Look carefully at each line of the conversation as you are going to write it out on Worksheet 8.

Notes for teachers

This worksheet is designed as an introduction to Worksheet 8 where the child will write the conversation that you dictate to her/him. You may like to act out this conversation with the child. To do this successfully it is a good idea to highlight each girl's comments in a different colour, colouring only the words that are spoken i.e. the words contained within the speech marks. Now look at the sentences carefully with the child. Encourage her/him to notice the features described on Worksheet 5 as well as the following:

• an exclamation mark is used where Daisy 'laughed' and where Maisy 'cried' because exclamation marks are used where someone shouts or speaks strongly

• apostrophes are used where letters are missed out e.g. 'it's' instead of 'it is'

• a new line is started where a different person speaks.

When you think the child is ready give her/him a copy of Worksheet 8.

worksheet
8

Listen to your teacher. Write the conversation that Maisy and Daisy are having on the telephone. The conversation has been started for you.

"Hello, is that Daisy?" said Maisy.
"Yes, who's that?" asked Daisy.

_____

_____

_____

_____

_____

_____

_____

_____

_____

_____

Notes for teachers
This worksheet should be used after Worksheet 7. You may decide to show the child Worksheet 7 again during the course of the dictation. Use Worksheet 7 for the dictation text and the rules that should be applied when the child writes. Before dictating the conversation to the child, remind her/him of the 'rules' from Worksheets 6 and 7 for writing down the conversation. As an extension activity, the child could continue the conversation further.

Name: _____ **Date:** _____

Look at some of the words from the conversations between Jim, Tom, Daisy and Maisy.

said   asked   laughed   cried   replied

These words come from root words. For example **said** comes from the word **say**.

Look at the root words below. Can you find words that come from them?

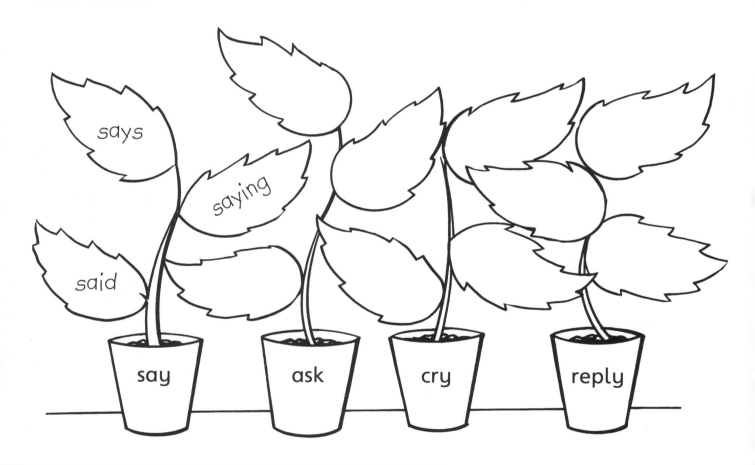

Notes for teachers

This worksheet follows Worksheets 5 to 8 and considers words that can be used in relation to speech. Help the child to think of words to write on the leaves and to spell them correctly. The words that s/he could find are: *asks, asked, asking, cries, crying, cried, replies, replying, replied*. The words *cry* and *reply* provide opportunities for discussing the rule that when the 'ed' ending is added to a word that ends in a consonant then 'y', the 'y' must be removed and be replaced by an 'i'. The child may not find all of the possible words but should be praised for those that s/he does find. Encourage her/him to try putting some of the words in sentences e.g. *"Is everybody here?" asks the teacher every day. "Have you done your homework?" the teacher asked. My friend was asking me to play football*. Note that not all the sentences contain speech marks. The final sentence of these three examples concerns indirect speech, i.e. it does not contain the exact words that were spoken. Help the child to focus on the word *said* and the words that end in 'ed' as these are the words that s/he is most likely to use in her/his written work. As an extension activity ask the child to write two or three sentences containing some of the 'ed' words.

Here are some more words that we use when writing down what people say.

shouted   whispered   called   answered

These words come from root words. For example **shouted** comes from the word **shout**.

Look at the root words below. Can you find words that come from them?

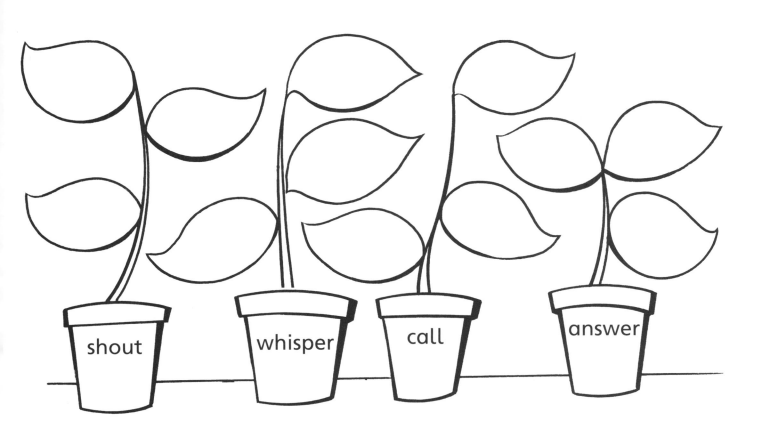

shout   whisper   call   answer

Notes for teachers
This worksheet focuses on more words that can be used in relation to speech. Help the child to think of words to write on the leaves and to spell them correctly. The words that s/he could find are: *shouts, shouting, shouted, whispers, whispering, whispered, calls, calling, called, answers, answering, answered*. S/he may not find all of these but should be praised for those that s/he does find. Discuss the fact that the words in the *answer* group all contain a silent 'w'. Encourage the child to try saying some of the words in sentences e.g. *My brother shouts too much. "Go away!" shouted my sister. The actor is shouting in the play*. Note that not all the sentences contain speech marks. The first and final sentences of these three examples do not contain direct speech. Help the child to focus on the words that end in 'ed' as these are the words that s/he is most likely to use in her/his written work. As an extension activity ask the child to write two or three sentences containing some of the 'ed' words.

Name: _____ **Date:** _____

Notes for teachers

This worksheet should be used after Worksheets 5 to 10. By now the child has seen how a conversation is written and has experienced writing conversations through the dictation exercises. The task on this sheet is for the child to write her/his own imaginary conversation using appropriately punctuated sentences. S/he will need some ideas for the subject of the conversation e.g. an invitation to a party, to the cinema, to go bowling, etc; a thank you call regarding a birthday present; a question about homework; etc. The task will be much easier if the child has had the opportunity to act out the phone conversation with another child or with an adult. Watch the child as s/he writes the sentences, prompting her/him to remember speech marks, capital letters, question marks, etc. Give lots of praise for any success in this difficult task.

Andrew Brodie: Supporting Writing Skills © A & C Black Publishers Ltd. 2007

Read the conversation that Ben and Jasdeep are having.

"Pass me the green paint," said Ben.

"I'm using it," said Jasdeep.

"But I need it," said Ben.

"You can't have it."

"I need it!" shouted Ben.

"I'm using it!" yelled Jasdeep.

"Ben and Jasdeep, come here!" demanded the teacher.

Notes for teachers

This worksheet is designed as an introduction to Worksheet 13 where the child will write the conversation that you dictate to her/him. You may decide to act out this argument with the child first. To do this successfully it is a good idea to highlight each child's speech in a different colour, colouring only the words that are spoken i.e. the words contained within the speech marks. Now look at the sentences carefully with the child. Encourage her/him to notice that:

• the words spoken are contained between the speech marks
• every sentence starts with a capital letter
• most of the sentences do not end at the end of the spoken section
• the closing speech marks are never alone – they always have a comma, an exclamation mark or a full stop before them
• different words are used before the speaker's name e.g. 'said', 'shouted', 'yelled', 'demanded'
• an exclamation mark is used where Ben 'shouted', where Jasdeep 'yelled' and where the teacher 'demanded' because exclamation marks are used where someone shouts or speaks strongly
• apostrophes are used where letters are missed out – 'I'm' instead of 'I am'; 'can't' instead of 'can not'
• a new line is started where a different person speaks

When you think the child is ready give her/him a copy of Worksheet 13.

Name: **Date:**

Listen to your teacher.

Write the conversation that Ben and Jasdeep are having.

The conversation has been started for you.

"Pass me the green paint," said Ben.

"I'm using it," said Jasdeep.

Notes for teachers

This worksheet should be used after Worksheet 12. You may like to show the child Worksheet 12 again during the course of the dictation. Before dictating the following to the child remind her/him of the 'rules' for writing down conversation from Worksheet 12.

"But I need it," said Ben.

"You can't have it."

"I need it!" shouted Ben.

"I'm using it!" yelled Jasdeep.

"Ben and Jasdeep, come here!" demanded the teacher.

As an extension activity, the child could continue the conversation further.

   Andrew Brodie: Supporting Writing Skills © A & C Black Publishers Ltd. 2007

Name: **Date:**

You are going to write an argument between two people.
Choose two people from the list below.

a policeman   a boy   a girl   a teacher

You have to decide what they are arguing about.
Here are some ideas for you to choose from.

    a ball   homework   a book   a bike

Notes for teachers

This worksheet should be used after Worksheets 12 and 13, which described an argument between two children over a pot of paint. The task on this sheet is for the child to write her/his own imaginary argument using appropriately punctuated sentences. Discuss the character choices with the child then talk about what they could be arguing about. Help the child to create a short dialogue then act it out together, perhaps jotting down some of the things that each person says. Explain that the argument needs to be written down in sentences that include speech marks and exclamation marks, if someone is getting cross or loud. Observe the child as s/he writes the sentences, prompting her/him to remember speech marks, capital letters, exclamation marks, etc. Give lots of praise for any success.

Name: **Date:**

Read the story.

Yesterday I took my dog for a walk on the beach.

Suddenly another dog appeared and Rex began to chase it.

"Come here, Rex!" I shouted.

Rex took no notice.

"Come here Penny!" called the other owner.

Penny took no notice.

The two dogs raced up and down the beach. Then they ran into the water and jumped in the waves. All the time they barked loudly.

When the dogs were tired I was able to catch Rex. I had to take him home to dry him.

Notes for teachers

This worksheet is designed as an introduction to Worksheet 16 where the child writes the story that you dictate to her/him. Unlike the previous worksheets, this text has some narrative as well as speech. Look at the sentences carefully with the child. Encourage her/him to notice that:

• not every sentence has speech marks because they are not all spoken sentences
• every sentence starts with a capital letter
• the words spoken are contained between the speech marks
• the closing speech marks are never alone – they always have an exclamation mark before them
• different words are used after the speaking e.g. 'shouted', 'called'
• an exclamation mark is used where the lady 'shouted', and where the other owner 'called' because exclamation marks are used where someone shouts or speaks strongly
• a new line is started after someone has spoken

When you think the child is ready give her/him a copy of Worksheet 16.

Andrew Brodie: Supporting Writing Skills © A & C Black Publishers Ltd. 2007

Name: **Date:**

Listen to your teacher. Write the story.
It has been started for you.

Yesterday I took my dog for a walk on the beach.
Suddenly another dog appeared and Rex began to chase it.
"Come here, Rex!" I shouted.
Rex took no notice.

Notes for teachers

This worksheet should be used after Worksheet 15. You may decide to show the child Worksheet 15 again during the course of the dictation. Before dictating the following to the child, remind her/him of the 'rules' for writing down the story from Worksheet 15.

"Come here Penny!" called the other owner.
Penny took no notice.
The two dogs raced up and down the beach. Then they ran into the water and jumped in the waves. All the time they barked loudly.
When the dogs were tired I was able to catch Rex. I had to take him home to dry him.

You may need to dictate the story several times. Encourage the child to write using the school's handwriting style. As an extension activity, Worksheet 17 contains comprehension questions related to the story.

Name: **Date:**

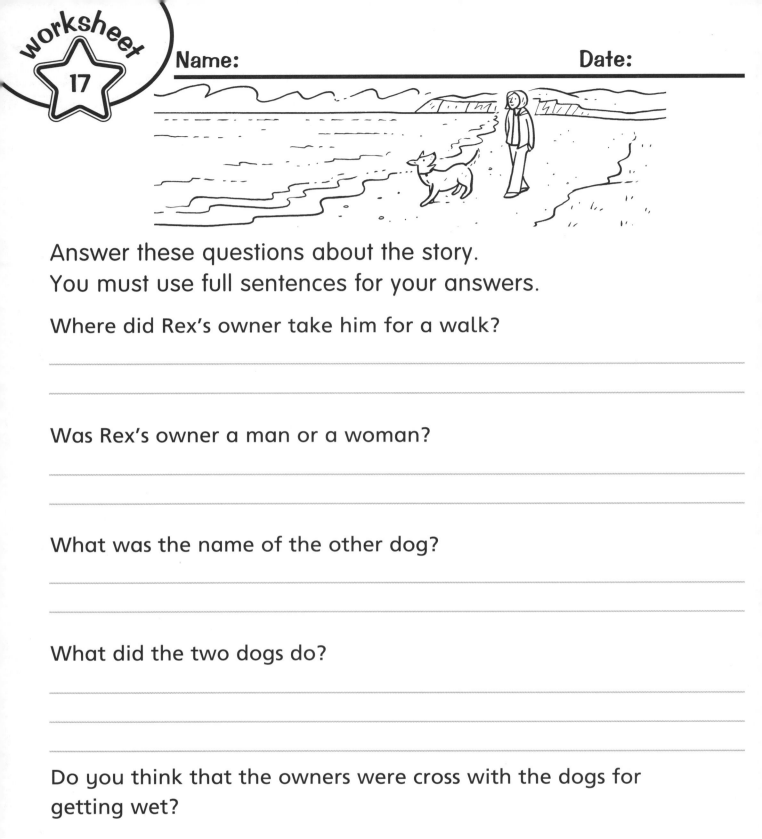

Answer these questions about the story.
You must use full sentences for your answers.

Where did Rex's owner take him for a walk?

_____

_____

Was Rex's owner a man or a woman?

_____

_____

What was the name of the other dog?

_____

_____

What did the two dogs do?

_____

_____

_____

Do you think that the owners were cross with the dogs for getting wet?

_____

_____

_____

Notes for teachers

This worksheet provides further practice in recognising and answering questions relating to the text and the illustrations for the story on Worksheet 15. Help the child to read the instructions then the question sentences. Point out that each sentence starts with a capital letter because all sentences do and that all the question sentences end with question marks. Discuss the apostrophe in the word 'Rex's' and why it is there (because the owner belongs to Rex!).

Encourage the child to write full sentences, ensuring that each starts with a capital letter and ends with a full stop e.g. for the first question the answer could be: *Rex's owner took Rex to the beach for a walk*. Discourage the child from writing short answers such as '*the beach*'. There are occasions when short answers are appropriate but our aim here is to help the child to recognise and write sentences. The final two questions could have answers that feature more complex sentences.

Andrew Brodie: Supporting Writing Skills © A & C Black Publishers Ltd. 2007

The story below has four paragraphs but they are written in the wrong order. Cut them out then arrange them in the correct order.

The shop assistant followed the man outside. "Stop!" she shouted.

I saw the man running towards me. I dropped my bags, the man tripped over them and the shop assistant grabbed him. I was a hero.

Yesterday I went shopping. In one shop I saw a man put a camera in his pocket. He left the shop so I told the shop assistant.

The man did not stop. He started to run. I saw him running around the corner of the street so I ran out of the back of the shop.

Notes for teachers

This worksheet provides excellent opportunities for reading practice as well as considerable speaking and listening. Help the child to read each paragraph then identify the first paragraph: *Yesterday I went shopping...* Can the child recognise that this is the first paragraph because it sets the scene? Help the child to notice the logical sequence of the other three paragraphs and to notice the ending of the final paragraph that serves to create a neat conclusion: *I was a hero*. On Worksheet 19 the child is asked to write out the story in the correct order.

Name: _____ **Date:** _____

Write out the story in the correct order. The first paragraph has been done for you.

Yesterday I went shopping. In one shop
I saw a man put a camera in his pocket.
He left the shop so I told the shop
assistant.

_____

_____

_____

_____

_____

_____

_____

_____

_____

_____

_____

_____

_____

Notes for teachers

This worksheet follows Worksheet 18. The child now knows the order of the paragraphs and can copy them to show the complete story. Help her/him to be accurate with both spelling and punctuation, while at the same time using the school's handwriting style. This is a lot for many children to remember and s/he will need praise for any successes. You may decide to take the opportunity to discuss the verbs that contain double letters: shopping, running, dropped, tripped and grabbed. These will be examined more closely on Worksheet 20.

 Andrew Brodie: Supporting Writing Skills © A & C Black Publishers Ltd. 2007

Name: _____ **Date:** _____

Look at some of the words from the shopping adventure story.

shopping   running   dropped   tripped

These words come from root words. For example **shopping** comes from the word **shop**.

Look at the root words below. Can you find words that come from them? Write the words on the leaves. Add extra leaves if you need to.

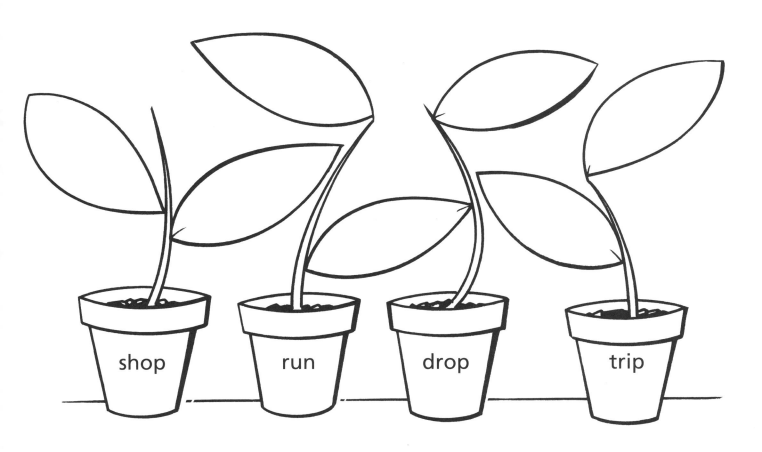

shop   run   drop   trip

Notes for teachers

This worksheet follows Worksheets 18 and 19 and focuses on words that are commonly spelt incorrectly. Help the child to think of words to write on the leaves and to spell them correctly. Encourage her/him to understand the rule that a word that ends with a vowel then a consonant usually needs an extra consonant when 'ing' or 'ed' is added. The words that s/he could find are: *shopping, shopped, running, runner, dropping, dropped, dropper, tripping, tripped, tripper*. S/he may not find all of these but should be praised for those that s/he does find. It might be helpful to the child to try some of the words in sentences. In this way s/he will hear that the word *runned* does not exist but that we use *ran* instead.

Name: _____   **Date:** _____

the thief

the shop assistant

the narrator

Read the shopping adventure story again. There are three characters in the story.

What do you think the thief might look like? Try to imagine him. Here are some ideas:

Is he tall or short or of average height?

Is he young, old or middle-aged?

Does he have long hair or short hair? Is his hair dark, fair, blond, brown, black, ginger, grey?

Does he have blue eyes, brown eyes, grey eyes or green eyes?

Is he clean-shaven or does he have a beard or a moustache?

Does he have dark skin or light skin?

What sort of clothes is he wearing? A coat? A jacket? A pullover? Black trousers? Blue trousers?

What are his shoes like?

Write a description of the thief.

_____

_____

_____

_____

_____

_____

_____

_____

_____

Notes for teachers

This worksheet follows Worksheets 18, 19 and 20. Read through the questions with the child, encouraging her/him to make decisions about the thief's appearance. This can be based on the illustration as well as the answers to the questions. S/he may have her/his own ideas and these should be encouraged. Help the child to write the description ensuring that s/he uses full sentences with appropriate punctuation.

Andrew Brodie: Supporting Writing Skills © A & C Black Publishers Ltd. 2007

Name: _____   **Date:** _____

Read the shopping adventure story again. There are three characters in the story.

the thief   the shop assistant   the narrator

What do you think the shop assistant might look like? Try to imagine her. Here are some ideas:

Is she tall or short or of average height?

Is she young, old or middle-aged?

Does she have long hair or short hair? Is her hair dark, fair, blond, brown, black, ginger, grey? Does she have a special hair-style? Does she wear anything in her hair, such as hair-clips or hair-bands?

Does she have blue eyes, brown eyes, grey eyes or green eyes?

Does she have dark skin or light skin?

Does she wear make-up?

What sort of clothes is she wearing? A coat? A jacket? A pullover? Trousers? A skirt? What colour are her clothes?

What are her shoes like?

Write a description of the shop assistant.

_____

_____

_____

_____

_____

_____

_____

_____

Notes for teachers

This worksheet follows Worksheets 18, 19 and 20. Read through the questions with the child, encouraging her/him to make decisions about the shop assistant's appearance. This can be based on the illustration as well as the answers to the questions. S/he may have her/his own ideas and these should be encouraged. Help the child to write the description ensuring that s/he uses full sentences with appropriate punctuation.

Have a look in a mirror.
What do you look like?
Draw a picture of yourself.

Write a description of your appearance
using the questions below to help you.

Are you a boy or a girl?

Are you tall or short or of average height?

How old are you?

Do you have long hair or short hair? Is your hair dark, fair, blond,
brown, black, ginger, grey? Do you have a special hair-style?

Do you have blue eyes, brown eyes, grey eyes or green eyes?

Do you have dark skin or light skin?

What sort of clothes are you wearing? School uniform? A jumper?
A shirt? Trousers? A skirt? What colour are your clothes?

What are your shoes like?

Notes for teachers
This worksheet follows Worksheets 21 and 22 where the child has written descriptions of imaginary people. Encourage
her/him to draw a self-portrait in the frame provided. Some children will be reluctant to do this as they lack confidence in
their drawing skills. If this is the case suggest that the child draws a complete picture of her/himself rather than just the head,
enabling the focus to be on the colour of the clothes, etc. Read through the questions with the child, encouraging her/him to
write clear answers using full sentences where appropriate. When s/he is ready help her/him to write the description.

Andrew Brodie: Supporting Writing Skills © A & C Black Publishers Ltd. 2007

Notes for teachers on Worksheets 24 to 28 and the Adjective bank sheets

Worksheets 24–28

The following pages are designed to help the child to write a story with clear beginning, middle and end sections.

To complete this task each pupil will need to roll a dice to insert certain words into her/his story. This is to enable children working in a group to have different stories whilst all having the same story structure. It also helps pupils to feel that there is a game-playing element to the task. The child may prefer to select one of the words to insert into their story rather than relying on the result of the dice roll.

After selecting a character in the first paragraph, the child will need to use this character in all three paragraphs. Show the child that in places in the story a choice will have to be made between the pronouns 'he' and 'she' according to the gender of the character.

Each page of the task represents one paragraph of the story. The child may need help in dealing with the asterisks that occur when the word s/he needs depends on a previous dice roll. The task results in a complete basic story.

Worksheets 27 and 28 can be photocopied (back to back on one sheet) to form a four-page booklet. On this, the child can write her/his completed story using the front as a title page and the following three pages for the story. S/he could use the paragraphs created on the three narrative sheets as a draft.

Adjective bank sheets 1–4

These resource sheets feature 'adjective banks' to encourage the child to use adjectives so that the final story is more interesting for the reader. These pages have a selection of adjectives on them so that you can help the child to find an adjective to use before each of the nouns in the story. Explain that adjectives are words that are used to describe things. You could add more adjectives in the extra spaces in the adjective banks. You could also use the words provided to start an adjective bank as a wall display to help with future writing.

Name: _____   Date: _____

You are going to write a story. We don't know who is in the story but we do know that the person finds something in the garden.

Roll a dice to find out how to write the first paragraph of the story. Find the correct word to match each roll of the dice from the words with pictures.

The Garden Mystery

One day a/an (**1**) _____ was in the garden (**2**)_____ . He/She was surprised to find a small (**3**) _____.
What should he/she do with it?

①

old man   young man   small boy   old lady   young lady   little girl

②

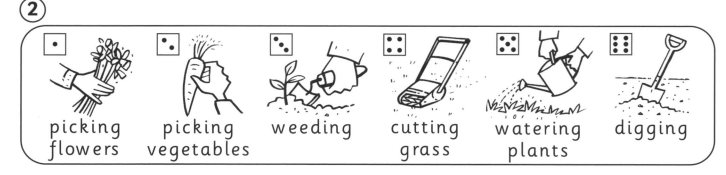

picking flowers   picking vegetables   weeding   cutting grass   watering plants   digging

③

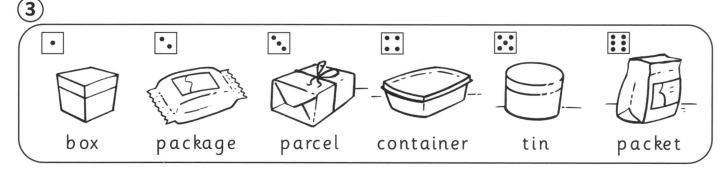

box   package   parcel   container   tin   packet

    Andrew Brodie: Supporting Writing Skills © A & C Black Publishers Ltd. 2007

Name: _____   **Date:** _____

Roll a dice to find out how to write the second paragraph of the story.

The * _____ thought about it. Then he/she
saw that it could be opened, so he/she opened it. Inside
was something wrapped in (**1**) _____ .
He/she unwrapped it and found a (**2**) _____ .
"How did this get into my garden?" he/she said.

* Where you see this star use the character from page one.

①

•	••	••	•• ••	•• • ••	•• •• ••
cardboard	bubble wrap	tissue	paper	cloth	wrapping paper

②

•	••	••	•• ••	•• • ••	•• •• ••
ring	watch	toy soldier	medal	toy dinosaur	brooch

Roll a dice to find out how to write the third paragraph of the story.

What a mystery thought the * _____ as he/she took the ** _____ into the (**1**) _____ .

A little later a boy came to the (**2**) _____ .

"Did I drop something in your garden?" he asked.

"I was taking it to school to show to my friends."

A few minutes later the boy went home. He was so pleased that his ** _____ had been found and he could take it to school the next day.

 * Where you see this star use the character from page one.

** Where you see two stars use the name of the item found in the garden.

①

⚀	⚁	⚂	⚃	⚄	⚅
house	shed	kitchen	lounge	bedroom	garage

②

⚀	⚁	⚂	⚃	⚄	⚅
door	house	gate	garden	roll again	roll again

Date:

The Garden Mystery

By

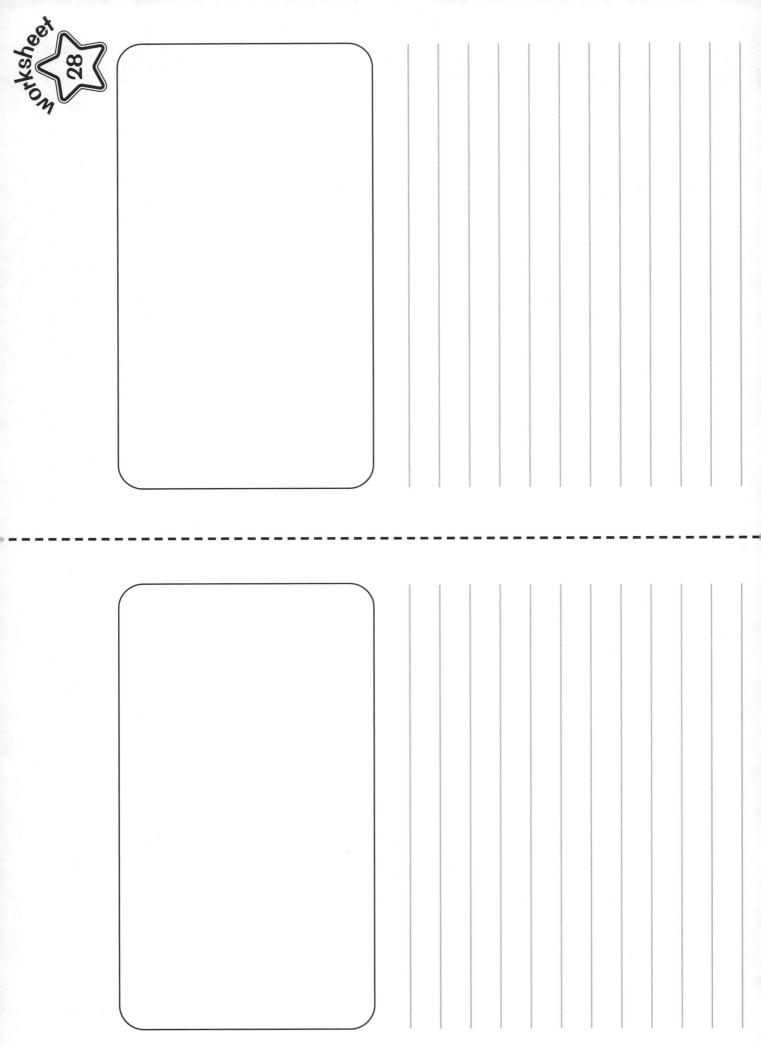

Andrew Brodie: Supporting Writing Skills © A & C Black Publishers Ltd. 2007

Adjective bank 1

beautiful	crumply
big	damp
black	dark
blue	dirty
bright	dull
brown	
cold	
colourful	

Adjective bank 2

dusty	helpful
friendly	hot
gigantic	huge
green	kind
grey	large
handsome	
happy	
heavy	

 Andrew Brodie: Supporting Writing Skills © A & C Black Publishers Ltd. 2007

Adjective bank 3

little	quiet
new	red
noisy	rusty
old	shiny
orange	short
pink	
pretty	
purple	

Adjective bank 4

small	warm
sparkling	wet
sparkly	white
spiky	yellow
strange	young
tall	
tiny	
ugly	

 Andrew Brodie: Supporting Writing Skills © A & C Black Publishers Ltd. 2007

Notes for teachers on Worksheets 29 to 35 and the Writing templates

The next seven pages focus on non-fiction writing. The subject of caring for a pet is tackled in a light-hearted way and through this task pupils are encouraged to think of particular aspects of pet care.

Worksheets 29–35

To complete this task the child will need to roll dice to insert certain words into her/his writing. This is to enable children working in a group to have different stories whilst all having the same written structure. It also helps pupils to feel that there is a game-playing element to the task. The child may prefer to select one of the words to insert into their story rather than relying on the result of the dice roll.

Each page of the task represents one aspect of pet care. The child may need help in dealing with the asterisks that occur when the word s/he needs depends on a previous dice roll.

The final part of the task is to ask the child to write about caring for a real pet. S/he will have learned what categories the writing could be divided into. The easiest way for the child to complete this task is to use the exact framework given for the fictitious creature, though it would be beneficial to add to this or to change aspects of it.

The four-page booklet that can be made from the final two sheets (34 and 35) photocopied back to back allows for the child to write about an aspect of pet care on each page.

You could encourage the child to undertake simple research using books or on the internet to find out facts about the pet s/he has chosen, or s/he may be working from personal experience of having a pet of her/his own.

Writing templates

Writing template 1 can be used for creating a four-page or eight-page book on any subject at any time. Simply photocopy this sheet on to both sides of a sheet of A4 paper then fold it to make a book, or use two sheets of A4 paper to make an eight-page book.

Writing template 2 can be photocopied to make a one-page A4 story sheet, again to be used at any time that you would like the child to produce a narrative or non-narrative piece of writing. The child can draw a picture at the top of the sheet then use the writing lines to write her/his own story.

Name: _____   **Date:** _____

You are going to write about caring for an imaginary pet. Find the correct word to match each roll of the dice from the boxes below.

Caring for a (1) _____

The *_____ is a (2) _____

(3)_____ legged creature with (4) _____

(5)_____ fur.

* Where you see this star use the pet's name from the first turn.

①

⚀	⚁	⚂	⚃	⚄	⚅
ziggle	chillick	stonky	digon	sottle	krish

②

⚀	⚁	⚂	⚃	⚄	⚅
large	small	tall	short	huge	tiny

③

⚀	⚁	⚂	⚃	⚄	⚅
two	three	four	five	six	eight

④

⚀	⚁	⚂	⚃	⚄	⚅
long	short	curly	silky	spiky	smooth

⑤

⚀	⚁	⚂	⚃	⚄	⚅
green	yellow	blue	purple	orange	red

      Andrew Brodie: Supporting Writing Skills © A & C Black Publishers Ltd. 2007

Roll a dice to find out how to write the second paragraph about caring for a pet.

Feeding

The *_____ likes to drink (**1**)_____.
This should always be available. This pet needs to
be fed (**2**)_____ each day.
It eats (**3**) _____ . Its food should be put
in a (**4**) _____ on the floor.

* Where you see this star use the pet's name from Worksheet 29.

①

⚀	⚁	⚂	⚃	⚄	⚅
water	tea	coffee	orange juice	milk	lemonade

②

⚀	⚁	⚂	⚃	⚄	⚅
once	twice	three times	four times	five times	six times

③

⚀	⚁	⚂	⚃	⚄	⚅
apples	toast	bananas	cabbage	eggs	potatoes

④

⚀	⚁	⚂	⚃	⚄	⚅
tin	dish	bowl	bucket	box	basket

Name: _____ **Date:** _____

Roll a dice to find out how to write the third paragraph about caring for a pet.

Exercise

A pet * _____ needs a good walk every (**1**) _____ . It walks very (**2**) _____ on a lead. The * _____ likes to play with a (**3**)_____ in the garden.

* Where you see this star use the pet's name from Worksheet 29.

①

⚀	⚁	⚂	⚃	⚄	⚅
day	week	year	month	evening	Sunday

②

⚀	⚁	⚂	⚃	⚄	⚅
quickly	fast	slowly	carefully	happily	well

③

⚀	⚁	⚂	⚃	⚄	⚅
ball	stick	kite	friend	boomerang	skipping rope

Re-write the paragraph about exercise using your best handwriting.

_____

_____

_____

_____

Andrew Brodie: Supporting Writing Skills © A & C Black Publishers Ltd. 2007

Name: _____ **Date:** _____

Roll a dice to find out how to write the fourth paragraph about caring for a pet.

Hygiene and grooming

The * _____ likes to be kept clean.
It needs to be (**1**) _____ every day. Always
wash your * _____ in (**2**) _____ .
Brush the pet with a (**3**) _____ . If you do
these things your * _____ will always look
and smell (**4**) _____ .

* Where you see this star use the pet's name from Worksheet 29.

①

⚀	⚁	⚂	⚃	⚄	⚅
washed	brushed	groomed	scrubbed	rinsed	bathed

②

⚀	⚁	⚂	⚃	⚄	⚅
soapy water	treacle	jam	orange juice	cold tea	gravy

③

⚀	⚁	⚂	⚃	⚄	⚅
toothbrush broom	hairbrush	paintbrush	nailbrush	scrubbing brush

④

⚀	⚁	⚂	⚃	⚄	⚅
wonderful	terrible	dreadful	lovely	awful	strange

Name: _____ **Date:** _____

Draw a picture of your pet * _____ .

Remember to make it look like its description on Worksheet 29. You may add extra features too. Here are some things to think about when drawing and colouring your picture.

Does the pet have a tail or horns? How many eyes and ears does it have? How long is its neck?

Your picture should be clearly labelled. Write your labels carefully. There are lines for you to write any other relevant things about this pet. Have fun!

* Where you see this star use the pet's name from Worksheet 29.

Andrew Brodie: Supporting Writing Skills © A & C Black Publishers Ltd. 2007

Date:

Caring for a

By

- -

Hygiene and grooming

Exercise

Feeding

 Andrew Brodie: Supporting Writing Skills © A & C Black Publishers Ltd. 2007

Writing template 1

Writing template 2

Andrew Brodie: Supporting Writing Skills © A & C Black Publishers Ltd. 2007

Notes for teachers on the Dictionary resource sheets

The dictionary that can be created from the final fourteen pages of this book is a very valuable resource. You may decide to practise the alphabet with the child before helping her/him to make the dictionary. An alphabet practice sheet is provided on page 50. Photocopy the fourteen Dictionary resource sheets to create master copies then photocopy the master copies, back to back, as follows:

Sheets 1/ 2   Sheets 3/4   Sheets 5/6   Sheets 7/8   Sheets 9/10   Sheets 11/12   Sheets 13/14

The dictionary contains all the high frequency and medium frequency words recommended for Key Stages 1 and 2, together with many of the additional words used in other books in this series.

Each page of the dictionary has spaces for pupils to write their own spellings. This is an excellent way of encouraging children to use their phonic knowledge to spell new words. When a child needs a word help her/him to find the correct page of the dictionary, then ask her/him to attempt the word by segmenting it into its phonemes. Give the child lots of praise where s/he is successful even with part of a word, then write the word correctly on the line next to her/his attempt, stressing the phonemes and pointing out the graphemes that represent these.

worksheet 38

Name: **Date:**

How quickly can you join the pairs of letters?
Draw a line to connect the **a** to the **A**, then another line to join
the **b** to the **B**, etc. Time yourself.

H   n   I   N   o   B

O   r   m   s   y   l   A   q

b   p   z   J   G   Z

     U   c   a   d   w

F   h   R   Y   S

X   T   Q   f   i   v   x

     u   j   V   W   E   P

K   M   g   C   k   L   D

     t   e

Notes for teachers
Revise the alphabet with the child, saying the names of the letters and the sounds that they make. Help her/him to join
the lower case letters to the matching upper case letters. Do not allow the child to complete the task in random order. Set
the challenge of completing the task as quickly as possible. This task can be repeated several times if appropriate as it
encourages the child to practise alphabetical order. It is essential that s/he can recognise the capital letter equivalent of
each lower case letter. Take the opportunity to introduce the dictionary created from the Resource sheets on pages
51–64, if you have not already done so. A further time challenge that can be set will be to see how quickly the child can
locate a particular page in this dictionary e.g. how quickly can s/he find the k page, the p page, the m page, etc?

          Andrew Brodie: Supporting Writing Skills © A & C Black Publishers Ltd. 2007

Dictionary

Name _____

Days	Months	Numbers	
Monday	January	1	one
Tuesday	February	2	two
Wednesday	March	3	three
Thursday	April	4	four
Friday	May	5	five
Saturday	June	6	six
Sunday	July	7	seven
	August	8	eight
	September	9	nine
	October	10	ten
	November	11	eleven
	December	12	twelve
		13	thirteen
		14	fourteen
		15	fifteen
		16	sixteen
		17	seventeen
		18	eighteen
		19	nineteen
		20	twenty

The alphabet

a A	n N
b B	o O
c C	p P
d D	q Q
e E	r R
f F	s S
g G	t T
h H	u U
i I	v V
j J	w W
k K	x X
l L	y Y
m M	z Z

Name

Address

Andrew Brodie: Supporting Writing Skills © A & C Black Publishers Ltd. 2007

Dictionary resource sheet 3

a A

a
able
about
above
across
address
adventure
afraid
after
afternoon
again
alarm
alien
all
almost
along
also
always
am
an
and
animals

another
answer
any
anyway
apartment
apple
are
arm
around
as
ask
asked
asking
assistant
at
autumn
average
away

x X

y Y

year
yell
yelled
yelling
yellow
yes
you
young
your

z Z

zero
zip

Dictionary resource sheet 4

b B

baby
back
ball
balloon
banana
bark
barked
battery
be
beard
beautiful
because
bed
been
before
began
being
below
better
between
bicycle
big
bike
birthday
bite
biting
black
blond
blue
boat
bonfire
both
boy
branch
break
breakfast
brick
bright
bring
brother
brought
brown
bulb
bungalow
but
by

w W

Wales
walk
walked
walking
want
was
watch
water
way
we
wear
wearing
weed
week
weekend
went
were
west
what
when
where
while
whisper
white
who
whole
why
will
window
winter
wire
with
without
woke
woken
woman
women
wood
word
work
world
would
wrap
write
writing
wrong
wrote

Andrew Brodie: Supporting Writing Skills © A & C Black Publishers Ltd. 2007

Dictionary resource sheet 5

v **V**

vegetables

very

village

---

c **C**

call

called

came

camera

can

canines

can't

caravan

cat

catch

caught

cereals

change

chase

cheek

chew

children

chin

cinema

city

clean

clean-shaven

clothes

colour

come

comes

coming

computer

corner

correct

could

country

countries

crazy

cricket

cried

cries

cry

Dictionary resource sheet 6

d D

dad

dark

day

daytime

demand

describe

description

dice

did

didn't

different

dig

do

does

dog

don't

door

down

downstairs

dressed

drop

dropped

drove

during

u U

ugly

under

uniform

United Kingdom

until

up

upon

upstairs

us

used

Andrew Brodie: Supporting Writing Skills © A & C Black Publishers Ltd. 2007

Dictionary resource sheet 7

t T

take	this
tail	those
teach	three
teacher	thought
teaches	through
teeth	tile
telephone	time
television	tired
tenth	to
than	today
thank	together
that	told
the	tongue
their	too
them	took
then	tooth
there	towards
these	town
they	trap
thief	trapping
think	tree
third	tries
	trip

tripped
trousers
trunk
trust
turn
turned
two

e E

ear
earlobe
early
earth
east
eleventh
England
enjoy
evening
ever
every
everybody
everything
eye
eyebrow
eyelashes
eyes

f F

fable	friends
face	from
family	front
father	fruit
favourite	
fifth	
fire	
fireworks	
first	
flat	
flew	
flower	
follow	
following	
foot	
football	
for	
found	
four	
fourth	
friend	
friendly	

s S

safe	show	starts
said	shower	stem
saw	sister	still
school	sixth	stop
Scotland	skin	stopped
second	skirt	stopping
see	sleep	straight
seen	slow	strange
seven	slowly	style
seventh	small	such
she	smooth	suddenly
shed	so	summer
shirt	some	sure
shoes	something	surprised
shop	sometimes	swimming
shopped	sound	swoop
shopping	south	
short	space	
should	sparkling	
shout	special	
shouted	spiky	
shouting	spring	
	started	

Andrew Brodie: Supporting Writing Skills © A & C Black Publishers Ltd. 2007

Dictionary resource sheet 9

r R

race

raced

ran

red

really

replied

replies

reply

right

roar

roof

roots

rope

round

run

running

g G

garage

garden

gave

get

ginger

girl

glass

go

goes

going

gone

good

got

grab

grabbed

great

green

grey

ground

growing

Dictionary resource sheet 10

h H

had
hair
half
halfway
happily
happiness
happy
has
have
he
head
heard
height
help
her
here
hide
high
him
his
hobbies
hobby

holiday
home
homework
hope
horrible
house
how
huge
hunting
hurry

q Q

question
quick
quickly
quiet
quietly
quite

Andrew Brodie: Supporting Writing Skills © A & C Black Publishers Ltd. 2007

Dictionary resource sheet 11

P p

paper
paragraph
people
pick
picture
pineapple
pink
place
play
please
pocket
police
possible
pot
potato
potatoes
pretty
probably
promise
protect
pull
pullover

purple
push
put

I i

I
I'm
if
imagine
important
impossible
in
incisors
inside
interesting
interview
Ireland
is
it

Andrew Brodie: Supporting Writing Skills © A & C Black Publishers Ltd. 2007

Dictionary resource sheet 12

j J

jacket

juice

jump

jumped

jumper

just

o O

o'clock

of

off

often

old

on

once

one

only

opened

or

orange

other

our

out

outside

over

owl

own

owner

Andrew Brodie: Supporting Writing Skills © A & C Black Publishers Ltd. 2007

Dictionary resource sheet 13

n N

name
narrator
near
neck
never
new
next
night
ninth
no
north
Northern Ireland
nose
nostril
not
notice
now
number

k K

kill
kitchen
knew
know

Dictionary resource sheet 14

L

ladder
lady
last
late
later
laugh
leaf
leap
leave
leaves
leg
lemonade
letterbox
light
like
lion
lip
little
live
lived
look
loud
loudly
lounge
love

m M

made
make
man
many
match
may
me
middle
middle-aged
might
minutes
mirror
molars
money
moral
more
morning
mother
mouse
moustache
mouth
much
mum
must
my
mystery

Andrew Brodie: Supporting Writing Skills © A & C Black Publishers Ltd. 2007